Master KS2 Reading with CGP!

When it comes to reading in Year 6, practice makes perfect.
That's why CGP have made this indispensable Question Book!

It's full of fascinating texts by a variety of authors —
each with practice questions to check pupils' understanding
and deepen their knowledge of techniques used by authors.

We've even included helpful answers at the back of the book.

What CGP is all about

Our sole aim here at CGP is to produce the highest quality books
— carefully written, immaculately presented
and dangerously close to being funny.

Then we work our socks off to get them out to you
— at the cheapest possible prices.

Contents

Published by CGP

Anthologist: Christopher Edge
Questions written by Amanda MacNaughton
Consultant: Julie Docker
Reviewers: Sam Bensted, Juliette Green, Maxine Petrie
Editors: Melissa Gardner, Kelsey Hammond, Christopher Lindle,
    Sam Norman, Gabrielle Richardson, Rosa Roberts

With thanks to Izzy Bowen, Alison Griffin, Sophie Herring and Holly Robinson for the proofreading.
With thanks to Ana Pungartnik for the copyright research.

ISBN: 978 1 78908 359 0
Printed by Elanders Ltd, Newcastle upon Tyne.

Text, design, layout and original illustrations
© Coordination Group Publications Ltd. (CGP) 2019
All rights reserved.

About this Book

This book consists of nine stimulating texts for pupils to read, with **two sets of questions** for each text:

- Question Set 1 checks that pupils understand the text as a whole, with lots of retrieval questions.
- Question Set 2 gets pupils thinking more deeply, with more questions requiring inference.

Question Pages

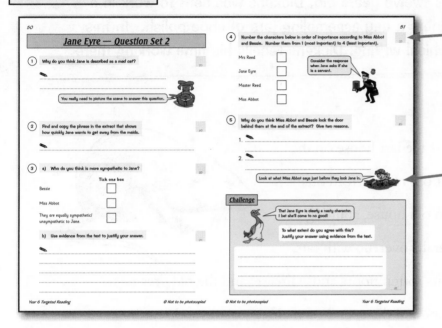

The **mark boxes** give the national curriculum content area for the question:

2B

Pupils are given tips on how to tackle some questions.

The recurring characters familiarise pupils with different types of question:

Scanning the text

Finding evidence in the text

National Curriculum References

Here is a key to the national curriculum references for the different question types:

2A   give / explain the meaning of words in context

2B   retrieve and record information / identify key details from fiction and non-fiction

2C   summarise main ideas from more than one paragraph

2D   make inferences from the text / explain and justify inferences with evidence from the text

2E   predict what might happen from details stated and implied

2F   identify / explain how information / narrative content is related and contributes to meaning as a whole

2G   identify / explain how meaning is enhanced through choice of words and phrases

2H   make comparisons within the text

At the back of the book, you'll find a table where you can record the pupil's performance in the different content areas:

			National Curriculum Content Areas							
			2a Word Meaning	2b Retrieval	2c Summarising	2d Inference	2e Prediction	2f Text Meaning	2g Language	2h Comparison
Text 1: Working in the Warehouse	Set 1			Q1 Q3 Q6		Q2			Q5	
	Set 2					Q2 Q3 Q4 Q5a Q5b		Q5b	Q1	
Text 2: Waste Warriors	Set 1		Q3	Q1 Q2 Q6	Q4			Q5		
	Set 2					Q2 Q5		Q1 Q5	Q3 Q4	
Text 3: Kidnapped	Set 1		Q4			Q3 Q5a Q6		Q2 Q5a		
	Set 2					Q2 Q5a Q3			Q4	

Working in the Warehouse

Start reading here. There might be important information in the introduction.

Charles Dickens is famous for his novels such as *A Christmas Carol* and *Oliver Twist*, however in his childhood his family faced hard times. When he was twelve years old, Dickens was sent to work in a warehouse for ten hours a day assembling jars of shoe polish. In this piece of autobiographical writing, Dickens recalls his time working there.

The blacking-warehouse was the last house on the left-hand side of the way, at old Hungerford Stairs. It was a crazy, tumble-down old house, abutting of course on the river, and literally overrun with rats. Its wainscoted rooms, and its rotten floors and staircase, and the old grey rats swarming down in the cellars, and the sound of their squeaking and scuffling coming up the stairs at all times, and the dirt and decay of the place, rise up visibly before me, as if I were there again. The counting-house was on the first floor, looking over the coal-barges and the river. There was a recess in it, in which I was to sit and work. My work was to cover the pots of paste-blacking;

first with a piece of oil-paper, and then with a piece of blue paper; to tie them round with a string; and then to clip the paper close and neat, all round, until it looked as smart as a pot of ointment from an apothecary's shop. When a certain number of grosses of pots had attained this pitch of perfection, I was to paste on each a printed label, and then go on again with more pots. Two or three other boys were kept at similar duty down-stairs on similar wages. One of them came up, in a ragged apron and a paper cap, on the first Monday morning, to show me the trick of using the string and tying the knot. His name was Bob Fagin; and I took the liberty of using his name, long afterwards, in Oliver Twist.

No words can express the secret agony of my soul as I sunk into the companionship of common men and boys. The deep remembrance of the sense I had of being utterly neglected and hopeless; of the shame I felt in my position; of the misery it was to my young heart to believe that, day by day, what I had learned, and thought, and delighted in, was passing away from me, never to be brought back, cannot be written.

I know I do not exaggerate, unconsciously and unintentionally, the scantiness of my resources and the difficulties of my life. I know that if a shilling or so were given me by anyone, I spent it in a dinner or a tea. I know that I worked, from morning to night, with common men and boys, a shabby child. I know that I tried, but ineffectually, not to anticipate my money, and to make it last the week through by putting it away in a drawer I had in the counting-house, wrapped into six little parcels, each parcel containing the same amount, and labelled with a different day. I know that I have lounged about the streets, insufficiently and unsatisfactorily fed. I know that, but for the mercy of God, I might easily have been, for any care that was taken of me, a little robber or a little vagabond.

An adapted extract from *The Life of Charles Dickens* by John Forster.

Discuss

In this text, Charles Dickens thinks back to the time in his life when he was poor. However, he went on to become a famous author. What do you think could have happened for him to change from working in a warehouse to being a famous novelist? Discuss your ideas with a partner.

Working in the Warehouse — Question Set 1

1 Which person is this autobiographical text written in?

2B

Tick one box

First person ☐

Third person ☐

2 Why was the warehouse where Dickens worked called the *blacking-warehouse*?

2D

✏ ....

....

> For this question, you will need to make links with what happens at the warehouse and what it is called.

3 Put these stages of Dickens's job into the correct order.

2B

Cover the pots with a piece of blue paper. ☐

Tie the papers round with string. ☐

Paste a printed label onto each pot. ☐

Cover the pots with oil-paper. ☐

Clip the paper close and neat all round. ☐

> For this type of question, first <u>find</u> each of the stages in the text and <u>underline</u> them. Then <u>number</u> them in the order they appear in the text. Finally, <u>match</u> each stage in the question to your numbered stages in the text.

© *Not to be photocopied*

4 Draw lines to match the words on the left (found in the text) with the most appropriate definition (on the right) for their context.

2A

abutting		shortage
wainscoted		freedom
apothecary		panelled in wood
liberty		next to
scantiness		person who prepares drugs/medicines

When you don't know what a word means, find it in the text and read around it to see what makes sense in the context.

5 Find three words and phrases in the text which show the warehouse was in a state of disrepair.

2G

If you're not sure what the word 'disrepair' means, think about the root word and the prefix.

Dictionary

1. ....

2. ....

3. ....

6 In your own words, summarise the final paragraph to show what life was like for Charles Dickens as a boy. The first sentence has been written for you.

2B

As a child, Charles Dickens had very little and life was tough.
....
....
....
....
....
....

8

Working in the Warehouse — Question Set 2

1 Which phrase in the paragraph beginning *The blacking-warehouse* shows that Charles Dickens is recalling memories from his childhood?

2G

....

2 Use the text to work out which of the following statements are true.

	True	False
There were only a few rats that lived in the warehouse.	☐	☐
Before applying labels, Charles Dickens had to cover a large number of pots with paper first.	☐	☐
Charles Dickens tried to ration out his wages.	☐	☐
Charles Dickens became a robber.	☐	☐

2D

3 Why do you think Bob Fagin was a name which Charles Dickens remembered such a long time after working in the warehouse?

2D

....

....

4 Which one of the following statements best summarises the paragraph beginning *No words can express...?*

2D

Tick one box

It is about the boredom Charles Dickens felt working at the warehouse. ☐

It is explaining the order of stages Charles Dickens had to follow to prepare the pots of polish. ☐

It describes how he felt about his childhood and life. ☐

It describes how he felt about working at the warehouse. ☐

> Summarising means looking at the whole section and putting it into just a few words.

Year 6 Targeted Reading

© *Not to be photocopied*

(5) a) **How do you think Charles Dickens felt about working in the warehouse?**

2D

✎

....

....

> Look forwards to part b) of the question. You're going to have to give three pieces of evidence from the text. It makes sense to think of an answer to part a) that there's plenty of evidence for.

b) **Find three words or phrases in the text that support your answer for part a).**

2F

1. ✎ ....

2. ✎ ....

3. ✎ ....

Challenge

> I wonder if working in the warehouse was fun? He must have been paid well if he worked all day — it can't have been that bad!

Explain to the bird why he's wrong.
Use evidence from the text to support your answer.

Why the bird is wrong	Evidence
....	....
....	....
....	....
....	....

2D

Waste Warriors

Sometimes a piece of writing can help persuade people to change their behaviour. In this online article, the author describes the environmental impact of waste plastic, and urges the reader to join a movement called 'Waste Warriors'.

WANTED: WASTE WARRIORS

Do you care about the environment in which you live? Are you **horrified** at the amount of plastic and waste that litters our planet and harms wildlife around the world? If so, we need you to be part of our Waste Warrior campaign!

Invasion of the Plastisphere

When plastic was invented, everyone was delighted to find a versatile material that didn't decompose. As a result of this, plastic has become a huge part of modern life, yet while this plastic revolution was taking place, no one stopped to think about what would happen when we disposed of it — until now, that is.

Did you know that approximately 150 million tons of plastic waste are currently floating around in our oceans, causing **untold damage** and death to many sea creatures? Since the 1950s, the use of plastic in the UK has grown and grown: we are now producing 5 million tons of plastic waste per year. All too much of this waste has been littered around our beautiful countryside, causing a massive blight on our surroundings and **immense danger** to animals, birds and plants.

When you go to the seaside, do you ever stop to consider the miles and miles of floating plastic pieces that engulf our amazing oceans? There is now even a name for these floating islands and the creatures that live on them — the Plastisphere. This word has had to be invented by scientists as it is only in our lifetimes that we have become aware of the shocking effect that plastic is having on our planet.

Is <u>this</u> how you see our future? A land submerged in perilous plastic and debris?

Not only do sea creatures get poisoned, injured or die from eating this unnatural substance, but the Plastisphere then ends up on our shores and unsuspecting land animals eat the plastic too. Do you think they deserve this **demise**? Or are you willing to do something to prevent it happening in the future?

Be a Warrior

We are calling upon concerned children with a conscience across the world to unite in our fight against the damage caused by **irresponsible disposal** of plastics. Do you have what it takes to be a Waste Warrior? Do you care enough about your environment and your future to educate and inspire others to follow our mission to eradicate plastic waste from our planet?

The first thing that you can do to save our planet is to reduce the amount of single-use plastic you use — things like plastic water bottles, plastic utensils, plastic straws and disposable food containers that you will only use once. You can encourage your friends and family to do the same, but if you really want to make a difference, you can become part of a fast-growing organisation that is determined to have a positive impact on the fight against plastic pollution.

Waste Warriors has been set up by like-minded individuals who can no longer just sit back and observe the dangers of plastic waste and the horrific blemish on our environment. Waste Warriors will be trailblazers in the battle to eradicate plastic waste from our oceans, cities, towns and countryside. We need children who will fully commit to our cause and join us in our worthwhile crusade.

> Visit our website here and register your interest. It will give you full details of what we have already achieved, and how you can be a part of the crusade against a plastic planet. **Please help us to make our world a better place**.

Written by Maxine Petrie

Consider

Think about how feelings have changed towards plastic since it was first invented. How would you try to persuade a company that produces plastic to think about the environment?

Year 6 Targeted Reading

Waste Warriors — Question Set 1

(1) Why did plastic make people happy when it was first invented?

....

....

(2) Draw lines to match each sentence (on the left) to the correct final word (on the right). Use the text to help you.

The Plastisphere is the name given to the miles and miles of plastic, and the creatures that live on it, which appear like floating	mission.
Eating plastic can poison, injure and kill both sea and land	containers.
The Waste Warriors movement aims to encourage children to join their	islands.
This text encourages you to use less single-use plastic, like water bottles, utensils and disposable	interest.
A link to their website is provided so that children can register their	creatures.

(3) Read the paragraph beginning *Did you know*. Find and copy two words which show that plastic is spoiling the environment.

1. ....

2. ....

> The question asks for two <u>words</u>. Don't be tempted to write any more than that.

4 Which of the following phrases best explains what is written about in the three paragraphs entitled *Be a Warrior*?

2C

Tick one box

how plastic has transformed the way that we live ☐

what can be done to help save the Earth from further damage ☐

what should have been done to remove plastics from the ocean ☐

Don't rush to answer questions like this. Read all three paragraphs again before you make your decision.

5 What three things could a child do to become a *Warrior* after reading this article?

2B

1. ....

2. ....

3. ....

6 Read the following statements and decide if they are a fact or an opinion.

2F

	Fact	Opinion
Approximately 8 million pieces of plastic waste are floating around our oceans.	☐	☐
The author believes that plastic waste has caused a massive blight on our surroundings.	☐	☐
Everyone should do something to help fight against the damage caused by plastic.	☐	☐
Floating islands of plastic waste and the creatures that live on them are called the Plastisphere.	☐	☐

If the statement could be reasonably argued against, it's probably an opinion.

Year 6 Targeted Reading

Waste Warriors — Question Set 2

1 Why do you think the author starts the text with questions?

2F

....

....

2 Use the section entitled *Invasion of the Plastisphere* to give two feelings the author has about plastic. Find evidence to support your answers.

2D

Author's feelings:	Evidence from the text:
1.	....
2.	....

> Abstract nouns like 'anger', 'excitement' and 'loneliness' are examples of words that show feelings.

3 Find and copy two phrases from the text which show the admiration the author has for planet Earth.

2G

1. ....

2. ....

> When it says 'Find and copy', don't write any words that aren't in the text. Make sure you copy the phrases carefully.

(4) In the caption underneath the picture of the seashore, the word *this* is underlined. Why has the author underlined that word?

2G

✏️

....

....

(5) Look at the words that are written in bold within the main text. Which of the following statements explains how they are linked?

2F

Tick one box

All of the words are metaphors. ☐

All of the words describe the plastic. ☐

All of the words show how bad the problem is. ☐

All of the words explain what pollution means. ☐

Challenge

I don't think the author should be asking children to become warriors: that's too dangerous! Children can't make changes anyway — only adults can.

Do you think the octopus is right? Say what you think, why you think it, and give evidence from the text to support your answer.

What I think:	....
Why I think it:	....
Evidence from text:	....

2D

Kidnapped

The following extract is taken from the novel *Kidnapped* by Robert Louis Stevenson, which was first published in 1886. This story is about a boy called David who has been sent to live with his Uncle Ebenezer after his parents have both died. Here, David's uncle has asked him to fetch a chest from the top of a tower in the house, but doesn't give David a candle to help light the way.

Out I went into the night. The wind was still moaning in the distance. It had fallen blacker than ever; and I was glad to feel along the wall, till I came the length of the stairtower door at the far end of the unfinished wing. I had got the key into the keyhole and had just turned it, when all upon a sudden, without sound of wind or thunder, the whole sky lighted up with wild fire and went black again. I had to put my hand over my eyes to get back to the colour of the darkness; and indeed I was already half blinded when I stepped into the tower.

It was so dark inside, it seemed a body could scarce breathe; but I pushed out with foot and hand, and presently struck the wall with the one, and the lowermost round of the stair with the other. The wall, by the touch, was of fine hewn stone; the steps too, though somewhat steep and narrow, were of polished masonwork, and regular and solid underfoot. Minding my uncle's word about the bannisters, I kept close to the tower side, and felt my way in the pitch darkness with a beating heart.

Well, as I advanced, it seemed to me the stair grew airier and I was wondering what might be the cause of this change, when a second blink of the summer lightning came and went. If I did not cry out, it was because fear had me by the throat; and if I did not fall, it was more by Heaven's mercy than my own strength.

It was not only that the flash shone in on every side through breaches in the wall, so that I seemed to be clambering aloft upon an open scaffold.

This was the grand stair! I thought; and with the thought, a gust of a kind of angry courage came into my heart. My uncle had sent me here, certainly to run great risks, perhaps to die. I swore I would settle that "perhaps," if I should break my neck for it; got me down upon my hands and knees; and as slowly as a snail, feeling before me every inch, and testing the solidity of every stone, I continued to ascend the stair. The darkness, by contrast with the flash, appeared to have redoubled; nor was that all, for my ears were now troubled and my mind confounded by a great stir of bats in the top part of the tower, and the foul beasts, flying downwards, sometimes beat about my face and body.

The tower, I should have said, was square; and in every corner the step was made of a great stone of a different shape to join the flights. Well, I had come close to one of these turns, when, feeling forward as usual, my hand slipped upon an edge and found nothing but emptiness beyond it.

An extract from *Kidnapped* by Robert Louis Stevenson.

Consider

Throughout this extract, we are made aware of David's feelings. The author doesn't use adjectives (e.g. 'afraid'); he describes the feelings in a more visual way. Find and underline any examples of this that you can find in this extract.

Kidnapped — Question Set 1

(1) Why was David heading to the top of the tower?

2B

....

(2) Find two phrases in the first paragraph which show how dark it is.

2G

1. ....

....

2. ....

....

(3) Why was David surprised when the whole sky lit up?

2D

....

....

(4) Draw lines to match the words from the text (on the left),
with a word from the right which could most suitably replace it.

2A

lowermost	openings
aloft	recalling
minding	perplexed
breaches	bottom
confounded	skyward

It helps to replace the words in the text with the synonyms given to see which one works best.

© Not to be photocopied

(5) a) *fear had me by the throat* is a phrase written in the third paragraph. What is this an example of?

Tick one box

simile ☐

noun phrase ☐

personification ☐

alliteration ☐

2G

b) What do you think the phrase *fear had me by the throat* means?

....

....

2D

> It's definitely worth re-reading the part of the text where this phrase appears, so you can be specific about why the author used this phrase.

(6) How did David feel about the bats at the top of the tower? How do you know?

2D

| How David felt: | .... |
| How I know: | .... |

> When you are asked how you know, you need to find evidence in the text.

Kidnapped — Question Set 2

(1) What do you think the *wild fire* was that lit the sky in the first paragraph?

2D

✎

....

(2) Circle the word below which best describes David's dominant feeling as he ascends the tower?

2C

confident   secure   cowardly   optimistic   threatened

(3) Find the paragraph which begins *This was the grand stair!* Why do you think the author chose to use the words *a gust of a kind of angry courage came into my heart*?

2G

✎

....

....

....

....

....

> Think about how the word 'gust' is usually used.

(4) David's feelings change throughout this extract. Which of the following lists most accurately reflects the order of his feelings?

2H

Tick one box

angry, distracted, dazed, afraid   ☐

distracted, afraid, dazed, angry   ☐

dazed, afraid, angry, distracted   ☐

dazed, angry, distracted, afraid   ☐

> Try and work out what his first feeling is — this will help you eliminate (get rid of) wrong answers.

Year 6 Targeted Reading   © *Not to be photocopied*

5 **a)** The introductory text says David's uncle has sent him to fetch a chest from the top of a tower in the house. Do you think this is the real reason he has sent him? Circle your answer.

2D

Yes   No

b) Give reasons to support your answer using evidence from the text.

2D

....
....
....
....
....
....

> When finding evidence, you do not need to write it in your own words. It's fine to copy phrases from the text.

Challenge

> I predict that David is going to find the chest and return it quickly and safely to his uncle.

Tick a box to show whether you agree or disagree with this statement. Then give a reason for your answer, supported by evidence from the text.

Agree ☐   Disagree ☐

....
....
....

2E

The Story of the Amulet

Remember to read the introduction. It might contain important information.

In a quest story, characters have to find something or achieve a specific goal. The following extract is taken from *The Story of the Amulet* by Edith Nesbit, which is about a group of children who find half of a magical amulet and set out on a quest to find the missing half. Here, Robert, Cyril and Anthea ask the charm where they will find its other half.

The room was dark. The world outside was dark - darker than the darkest night that ever was. And all the sounds went out too, so that there was a silence deeper than any silence you have ever even dreamed of imagining. It was like being suddenly deaf and blind, only darker and quieter even than that.

But before the children had got over the sudden shock of it enough to be frightened, a faint, beautiful light began to show in the middle of the circle, and at the same moment a faint, beautiful voice began to speak. The light was too small for one to see anything by, and the voice was too small for you to hear what it said. You could just see the light and just hear the voice.

But the light grew stronger. It was greeny, like glow-worms' lamps, and it grew and grew till it was as though thousands and thousands of glow-worms were signalling to their winged sweethearts from the middle of the circle. And the voice grew, not so much in loudness as in sweetness (though it grew louder, too), till it was so sweet that you wanted to cry with pleasure just at the sound of it. It was like nightingales, and the sea, and the fiddle, and the voice of your mother when you have been a long time away, and she meets you at the door when you get home.

And the voice said —

'Speak. What is it that you would hear?'

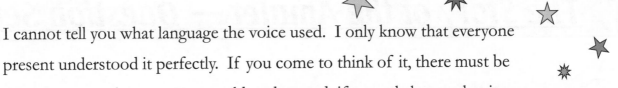

I cannot tell you what language the voice used. I only know that everyone present understood it perfectly. If you come to think of it, there must be some language that everyone could understand, if we only knew what it was. Nor can I tell you how the charm spoke, nor whether it was the charm that spoke, or some presence in the charm. The children could not have told you either. Indeed, they could not look at the charm while it was speaking, because the light was too bright. They looked instead at the green radiance on the faded Kidderminster carpet at the edge of the circle. No one cared to speak.

It was Cyril who said at last —

'Please we want to know where the other half of the charm is.'

'The part of the Amulet which is lost,' said the beautiful voice, 'was broken and ground into the dust of the shrine that held it. It and the pin that joined the two halves are themselves dust, and the dust is scattered over many lands and sunk in many seas.'

'Oh, I say!' murmured Robert, and a blank silence fell.

'Then it's all up?' said Cyril at last; 'It's no use our looking for a thing that's smashed into dust, and the dust scattered all over the place.'

'If you would find it,' said the voice, 'you must seek it where it still is, perfect as ever.'

'I don't understand,' said Cyril.

'In the Past you may find it,' said the voice.

An extract from *The Story of the Amulet* by Edith Nesbit.

Discuss

The end of the extract suggest the children are going to have to go back in time. How do you think they will try and do this? Come up with a few ideas of how children could time-travel in a story. Which of your ideas is best?

Year 6 Targeted Reading

The Story of the Amulet — Question Set 1

(1) **What is the Amulet?**

2B

✏️

....

(2) **Use the extract to help you identify whether the following statements are true or false.**

2B

	True	False
The light came after the voice.	☐	☐
At first the light was lovely and large.	☐	☐
The children were surprised how dark it was.	☐	☐
The light came from many glow-worms.	☐	☐

> For this question you will need to read the text very carefully. Don't just skim read.

(3) **Write down four things that the voice is compared to.**

2B

1. ✏️ ....

2. ✏️ ....

3. ✏️ ....

4. ✏️ ....

4 Which of the following words could replace the word
radiance in the sentence beginning *They looked instead?*

2A

Tick one box

illumination ☐

haziness ☐

shadow ☐

outline ☐

> If you're stuck,
> try reading the
> sentence again and
> replacing the word
> 'radiance' with
> each of the options
> given on the left.

5 Why do the children think it is not worth looking for the lost part of the Amulet?

2B

✏ ....

....

6 Number the following events in the order they occur in the text.

2C

Cyril is confused. ☐

The children are in darkness. ☐

Cyril and Robert react to the voice's
explanation of what happened to the Amulet. ☐

The light grows stronger. ☐

The voice begins to speak more loudly. ☐

> You need to find the secret
> code. First <u>find</u> and <u>underline</u>
> each event in the text.
> <u>Number</u> the events in the
> order they happen in the text.
> Then <u>match</u> each event in
> the question with the number
> you've written in the text.

26

The Story of the Amulet — Question Set 2

1 **a)** In the first paragraph, different forms of the word 'dark' are used. Write them below.

2B

1. .... 2. .... 3. ....

b) What is the effect of repeating these different forms of the word 'dark'?

2G

Asking 'what is the effect' is like asking what it makes the reader think, imagine or feel.

....

....

2 Write down one thing that the light is compared to in the text.

2B

The light is compared to ....

3 What effect does the Amulet have on the children? Use evidence from the text to support your answer.

2D

Effect on children:	....
	....
Evidence from text:	....
	....

This question is asking how you think they feel. This means there is no wrong or right answer, but you must be able to justify your answer with evidence from the text.

© *Not to be photocopied*

4 We are told the Amulet was once held in a *shrine*.
Which of the following is the best definition of a shrine?

2A

Tick one box

A place which gives out a shining bright light. ☐

A place full of beautiful flowers. ☐

A place which is sacred or holy. ☐

A place where people sing. ☐

5 Use the information given in the extract to write a description of the Amulet in your own words. Remember to mention its voice, its light and anything else the extract has referred to about the Amulet.

2C

....

....

....

....

Underline the parts of the text that will help you to answer this question.

Challenge

So to find the other half of the Amulet, the children are going to have to find every piece of dust that it smashed into and try and put it together? I don't think that will be very easy!

Convince the lion that this is not what the children will be doing. Using evidence from the end of the text, suggest what they might have to do instead.

....

....

....

2D

Air Raids

A non-chronological report gives readers information about a topic, but isn't written in time order. The following report about air raids in the Second World War includes a timeline, but also presents information using subheadings, pictures and fact boxes.

Air Raids

World War II was the first war in which mass air attacks targeted the civilian population in built up areas. Cities in Europe and Japan suffered heavy bombing. For many children, air raids became part of daily, and nightly, life.

Britain was bombed by German planes in 1940-1941. This bombardment became known as the Blitz (from the German Blitzkrieg, meaning "lightning war"). There were more air raids in 1944, this time by V-1 flying bombs and V-2 rockets. From 1942, German cities were heavily bombed by British and American planes. In the Pacific, Japanese planes bombed some Australian towns, while American bombers attacked Tokyo and other Japanese cities.

Air raid shelters were designed to protect people from bomb-blasts. This is a public shelter in New York, in the United States. Although the United States prepared for air raids, neither Japan nor Germany had bombers that could fly far enough to bomb US cities on the mainland.

Living with the bombs

There were fears that bombing would create mass panic, but most people just carried on with their daily lives. Children went to school, and during air raids slept in air raid shelters instead of bedrooms. Air raids were often at night, so children had to be woken and taken to the shelter when the sirens gave the alarm. Many people stayed at home during air raids, while others spent the night in shelters. Thousands slept in Chislehurst Caves in Kent, England, while many Londoners slept in London Tube (Underground) stations.

Raids on Germany

German children experienced the terrors of air raids almost constantly in 1944-1945. In Berlin, people crammed the U-Bahn (underground) stations. With as many as 5,000 people crowded into shelters meant for 1,500, it was very uncomfortable. People lit candles to check if the air was being used up. If a candle on the ground went out, children had to be picked up and held at shoulder height, where there was more oxygen. At times, the air got so bad that everyone had to leave, even while the bombs were still falling.

A British bombing plane

WWII bombing casualties	
Australia	several hundred
Britain	over 60,000
China	over 560,000
Germany	600,000
Japan	over 400,000
Soviet Union	over 500,000
United States	over 2,000 (in Hawaii)

September 1940

The German Luftwaffe begins its bombing raids on London. Known as the Blitz, it reaches its climax in 1941.

1940–1941

Raids on Coventry and many other British cities damage thousands of houses and many schools.

1942

Allied air forces begin round-the-clock bombing of Germany: the RAF by night, the USAAF by day.

June–September 1944

Britain is hit by German V-1 flying bombs. A new evacuation begins with over 1 million people moving out of London.

February 1945

Allied air raids on the German city of Dresden kill at least 30,000 people.

6 and 9 August 1945

Two US atomic bombs wipe out the Japanese cities of Hiroshima (over 100,000 killed) and Nagasaki (over 40,000 killed).

An extract from *Children During Wartime* by Brenda Williams.

Discuss

Imagine you had to spend a night in one of the public air raid shelters (in Germany or in Britain). What do you think it would feel like? What might happen? What sights and sounds might you hear?

Air Raids — Question Set 1

(1) Name one country that each of the following countries bombed.

2B

Britain	....
United States	....
Japan	....
Germany	....

(2) Why was the United States mainland not bombed?

2B

....

(3) Draw lines to match the people (on the left) with something they did during the Second World War (on the right).

2B

Londoners	were held at shoulder height in the shelters.
German children	began bombing London in September 1940.
The German Luftwaffe	slept in the underground tube stations of the city.
British children	were crowded and uncomfortable in the U-Bahn stations.
German people	continued to go to school during the day.

If two answers seem possible, match up all the other pairs first to see which one is left over.

Who?
What?
Where?
When?
Why?

④ **Read the statements below and decide whether they are facts or opinions.**

	Fact	Opinion
German children found the war much harder to deal with than British children.	☐	☐
Some people chose to stay in their homes during air raids.	☐	☐
It was really unfair that some people had to sleep in caves when others got to sleep in air raid shelters.	☐	☐
More Japanese people were killed than British people.	☐	☐
America was the luckiest country during World War II.	☐	☐

⑤ **Find a synonym in the text for each word below.**

extensively	....
widespread	....
packed	....
peak	....

⑥ **What does the phrase 'wipe out' suggest about the bombing of Hiroshima and Nagasaki in 1945?**

✏ ....

Air Raids — Question Set 2

(1) Write a short summary for the paragraphs shown in the table below. The first one is done for you.

2C

Paragraph	Summary
'Britain was bombed...'	It tell us which countries bombed which other countries in World War II.
'There were fears that...'	....
'German children experienced...'	....

(2) Read the information below. Add a suitable subheading to these paragraphs.

2C

 ....

Anderson Shelters were made from corrugated sheets of iron and half buried in the ground with earth piled on top of them. Thousands were issued by the government. Inside they were dark, damp and uncomfortable to sleep in.

For those who did not have gardens, Morrison Shelters were designed. They stayed in people's homes, could be used as tables and were made of steel.

Giving a subheading is like summarising the text in a few words.
The subheading you choose needs to be appropriate for <u>both paragraphs</u>.

(3) Find two phrases in the text which reflect the destruction caused by the air raids.

2G

1. ....

2. ....

4 Who do you think this report is aimed at and why?

2F

✏

....

....

....

....

> Think about what sort of people the report talks about most and also what sort of ideas the author explains. This might help you think about what sort of reader they have in mind.

5 Use evidence from the text to explain why you think Germany had the most casualties from air raids in World War II.

2H

✏

....

....

....

....

Challenge

> German and British children must have been quite excited about camping out in the air raid shelters.

> Do you agree or disagree? Explain why you think this using evidence from the text to support your answer.

....

....

....

....

....

....

2D

Text 6 — Flashback Story

The Girl of Ink & Stars

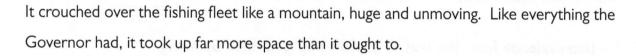

A flashback is a technique authors use to take readers back to an earlier time in a story. The following extract is taken from the novel *The Girl of Ink & Stars* by Kiran Millwood Hargrave, which is about a girl named Isabella who lives on the island of Joya. Here, Isabella is walking to school and looks out at a ship moored in the harbour which belongs to the governor of the island.

It crouched over the fishing fleet like a mountain, huge and unmoving. Like everything the Governor had, it took up far more space than it ought to.

To the east, his house glinted in the sunrise. Built from black basalt and big as five ships, the mansion sat between the blue sea and the green forest, spreading out over the fields like a storm cloud. From here, though, it looked small enough to squash between my forefinger and thumb. Below it was the village, with the school halfway between.

The old school building had been small but bright, and we had painted the walls rainbow colours with whatever dyes Da could spare. But then the Governor had knocked it down — Lupe had decided she'd had enough of being taught alone at home and demanded to be sent to the local school like the rest of us.

Governor Adori had rebuilt it from stone, twice as big, because if his daughter was going, it had to look grander.

"Not for me, you understand," said Lupe with a sad smile. She adopted an even posher voice to add, "To uphold the family honour."

We weren't allowed to paint the walls of the new school. A lot of children were unkind to Lupe because of that, but I knew it wasn't her fault.

Behind the Governor's house, closest to the forest, were the orchards, where I had never been. I squinted at the ant-like specks of the labourers there and wondered which one was Pablo. To the west, the black sand of the beaches was almost covered by the incoming tide. We were not permitted to be on the beaches at high tide, and no one was allowed in the sea unless they were launching one of the Governor's boats. My toes itched. Da had described being in the sea, but it was not the same as trying it for myself.

Above the beaches were the clay mines, which I tried not to look at because it brought back one of the few clear memories I had of Ma — the day she took Gabo and me to the mines. She taught us how to tie ourselves with vines to a dragon tree — You knot like this, and then rub the sap into your hands for grip — and lowered us one by one into the gorge. Gabo got scared and wriggled so much the knot broke. When he landed on the soft mud at the bottom, it made a very rude noise, and he was filthy when Ma climbed up with him from the darkness.

I laughed so hard it hurt.

I remembered that, that ache in my belly. How it came back two months later, when Ma died. Only then it was sharper, and there was no one carrying anyone out of that darkness. Three years later, the same sweating sickness took Gabo. Three years after that, the clay mine memory still made my throat feel tight.

An extract from *The Girl of Ink & Stars* by Kiran Millwood Hargrave.

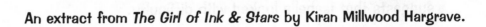

Consider

Think of a time when you had fun with your family or friends. What makes it such a memorable time? How would you describe it? Remember to include feelings and reactions as well as description of what happened.

Year 6 Targeted Reading

The Girl of Ink & Stars — Question Set 1

1 Draw lines to match the place with where it is located on the island of Joya.

2B

The Governor's house		Further away from the beach than the Governor's house
The school		Above the beaches
The orchard		To the west
The beaches covered by the tide		Between the Governor's house and the village
The clay mines		Between the sea and the forest

Match the ones you are sure of first.

Who?
What?
Where?
When?
Why?

2 How does Isabella know Lupe?

2B

....

....

Scan the text for when Lupe is first mentioned to know where to start reading from.

3 Put a tick next to the word from the text that suggests that Isabella looked with difficulty.

2A

glinted ☐   itched ☐

adopted ☐   covered ☐

squinted ☐   wriggled ☐

4 | **Number the following events from the story in the order they happen.**

2C

Isabella remembers being at the clay mines. ☐

Isabella laughs so hard it hurts. ☐

Isabella's Ma dies. ☐

Gabo dies. ☐

> When a story uses a flashback, the order of events might be different to the order they appear in the text.

5 | *It crouched over the fishing fleet like a mountain, huge and unmoving. Select a word or short phrase from this sentence which demonstrates each language feature mentioned below.*

2G

1. similie: ....

2. personification: ....

6 | **What is Isabella's flashback about?**
Mention at least three things that happen in the flashback.

2B

....

....

....

....

....

....

....

Year 6 Targeted Reading

The Girl of Ink & Stars — Question Set 2

1 From reading the extract, try and work out if the following statements are true or false.

2D

	True	False
The Governor is rich.	☐	☐
Lupe is popular at school.	☐	☐
Isabella feels sorry for Lupe.	☐	☐
Isabella wants to swim in the sea.	☐	☐
Ma and Gabo die of different diseases.	☐	☐

The text won't tell you exactly if these are true or false. You will have to do a bit of digging to work them out.

2 The extract contains the phrase: *the ant-like specks of the labourers there.* What does this phrase suggest about the workers that Isabella can see?

2G

....

3 a) Why are the other children unkind to Lupe?

2B

....

....

b) What do you think Lupe's opinion is of her Dad? Use evidence from the text to support your answer.

2D

....

....

....

....

....

4 Find and copy two words or phrases from the extract that show Isabella's desire to go in the sea.

2G

1. ....

2. ....

5 What is the difference in meaning between the following two quotes from the extract?

2H

| climbed up with him from the darkness | | carrying anyone out of that darkness |

....

....

....

....

....

One of these quotes is talking about <u>literal</u> darkness. The other one is using darkness as a <u>metaphor</u>.

Challenge

It sounds beautiful on the island of Joya. Isabella must love looking at the scenery, especially the clay mines.

Do you agree with the jellyfish? Use evidence from the text to support your answer.

....

....

....

....

....

2D

Year 6 Targeted Reading

Lasers

Remember to read the introduction. It might contain important information.

An effective explanation can help you to understand important information in a clear and concise way. In this extract from *The Encyclopedia of Science*, the author explains the science and the applications of lasers.

What is a laser?

A laser is a machine which turns an ordinary beam of light into a straight, narrow beam of very bright light. Laser light does not spread out like ordinary light, so it is concentrated and very powerful. It can cut through steel and human tissue, and can be used to measure distances accurately, make holograms and compact discs, or guide missiles. Lasers usually produce light of a particular type, e.g. light of one colour only or invisible infra-red rays. All the waves are in step, and reinforce each other, which is why they are so powerful, and can travel long distances without fading.

Inside a laser is a tube filled with a gas, a solid or a liquid, called the active medium. This can be a man-made crystal, like ruby. Energy, such as light from a flash tube, is passed through the active medium, making it give off light. Some of this bounces to and fro between two mirrors, making the active medium give off even more light.

This is called lasing. The beam of concentrated light then escapes through the partially mirrored surface, emerging as a laser beam.

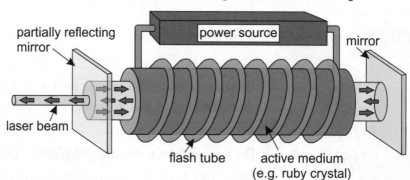

partially reflecting mirror

power source

mirror

laser beam

flash tube

active medium (e.g. ruby crystal)

Investigating the Earth

Lasers have been very useful in increasing knowledge about our planet. The distance from the Moon to the Earth was measured by bouncing a laser beam off a reflector on the Moon. Lasers reflected off satellites orbiting the Earth can also detect tiny land movements on our planet. Scientists can use this data to measure the movements of continents or to detect earthquakes and volcanic eruptions.

Futuristic weapons

Although laser weapons are relatively new on the scene in real life, imaginative science fiction writers and filmmakers have incorporated lasers into their works for a long time. Laser weapons appear in the James Bond movie Goldfinger (1964), which was based on a book by Ian Fleming (1908–1964). Lasers also feature in the Star Wars films, where they are fired from guns and used as swords.

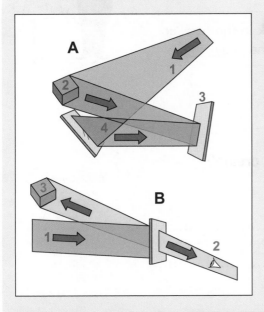

Holograms

A laser beam can be used to record a ghost-like three-dimensional image called a hologram. The laser beam (1) is split into two parts. One part is aimed at the object (2), and the reflected light, called the object beam, illuminates the film (3). The other part, called the reference beam (4), is reflected by a mirror before illuminating the film. Where the two beams meet on the film, a hologram is formed. In figure B, a beam of light identical to the reference beam (1) is directed at the developed film. A viewer (2) sees the image (3) in three dimensions.

History of the laser

1960 The first laser was developed by a scientist called T.H. Maiman.	1988 First transatlantic optical fibres send telephone messages.
1961 First commercially-built laser sold.	1991 Laser-guided missiles used by USA in Gulf War.
1961 First laser holograms developed.	1998 Experimental high-power microlasers are developed. They are so small that hundreds could fit on the head of a pin.
1963 Lasers first used in surgery.	
1976 Lasers used to measure Earth's movements.	2003 NASA flies a plane powered by lasers.
	2014 First cars available with laser headlights.
1982 Compact discs launched.	2019 Lasers used to amplify whispers. They could be used to send secret messages.

An adapted **extract** from *The Encyclopaedia of Science.*

Consider

A <u>kenning</u> is a two-word phrase which describes an object (often using metaphors). For example, here are some kennings for 'winter': 'Snow faller', 'Face freezer', 'Christmas bringer'.
Think of some two-word phrases you could use to describe a laser.

Year 6 Targeted Reading

Lasers — Question Set 1

(1) What does a laser do to an ordinary beam of light?

2B

✎
....

....

> This question doesn't tell you <u>where</u> to look in the text, so you'll need to read through the text from the <u>beginning</u>.

Who?
What?
Where?
When?
Why?

(2) How does the author describe the light that lasers create?

2B

✎
....

....

(3) The words given on the left can be found in the text.
Draw lines to match up each word with a correct definition
(given on the right) for the context of the writing.

2A

medium		not completely
orbiting		lights up
partially		revolving around
illuminates		substance

> You'll need to match words of the <u>same word class</u> in this question. The <u>endings</u> of the words might give you a few clues.

4 Use the text to decide if the following statements are true or false. Tick your answer.

2C

	True	False
Lasers are used by scientists to study the Earth.	☐	☐
Lasers only have one important job to do.	☐	☐
Lasers have only been discovered in the last 20 years.	☐	☐
Laser light waves are different to ordinary light waves.	☐	☐

5 Explain why you think the author has used subheadings within this text.

2F

....

....

When you're asked about layout features, think about how they are useful to the reader.

6 Lasers have been an important development in the world's history. Find and copy three phrases from the text which support this view.

2G

1. ....

2. ....

3. ....

Lasers — Question Set 2

1 A laser beam can be used to record a ghost-like three-dimensional image called a hologram.
What does the word *ghost-like* tell you about a hologram's appearance?

2G

....

....

2 Why do you think the author has chosen the subheading *Futuristic weapons* for the paragraph which talks about lasers in films made in the past?

2D

....

....

3 Read the following phrases and decide if they are describing ordinary light waves or laser light waves.

2H

	Ordinary light	Laser light
are spread out so less powerful	☐	☐
can be one colour only	☐	☐
can travel far and stay concentrated	☐	☐
reinforce each other	☐	☐
do not all follow the same path	☐	☐

Don't forget to use the diagrams as well as the text to help find your answers.

4 Name two ways in which the diagram of green and yellow light beams containing arrows and pink blocks is related to the text about holograms.

1. ....

....

2. ....

....

> When diagrams and text are related, they have certain things in common.

5 In your own words, how would you describe the development of the laser from 1960 to 2019. Use the text to support your answer.

....

....

....

Challenge

> Lasers are so important! Without them, the films we watch wouldn't be so exciting.

> Do you agree that is why lasers are so important? Use evidence from the text to support your answer.

What I think:	....
Why I think it:	....
Evidence from the text:	....

Jane Eyre

This extract is from the novel *Jane Eyre* by Charlotte Brontë. The novel follows the life of an orphan, Jane, through an unhappy childhood living with her cruel, rich aunt, into adulthood. Here, she is being scolded for hitting her cousin.

"Hold her arms, Miss Abbot: she's like a mad cat."

"For shame! for shame!" cried the lady's maid. "What shocking conduct, Miss Eyre, to strike a young gentleman! Your young master."

"Master! How is he my master? Am I a servant?"

"No; you are less than a servant, for you do nothing for your keep. There, sit down, and think over your wickedness."

They had got me by this time into the apartment indicated by Mrs. Reed, and had thrust me upon a stool: my impulse was to rise from it like a spring; their two pair of hands arrested me instantly.

"If you don't sit still, you must be tied down," said Bessie. "Miss Abbot, lend me your garters; she would break mine."

Miss Abbot turned to remove a garter from her stout leg. This preparation for bonds, and the additional shame it inferred, took a little of the excitement out of me.

"Don't take them off," I cried; "I will not stir."

In guarantee of which, I attached myself to my seat by my hands.

"Mind you don't," said Bessie; and when she had ascertained that I was really subsiding, she loosened her hold of me; then she and Miss Abbot stood with folded arms, looking darkly and doubtfully on my face, as incredulous of my sanity.

"She never did so before," at last said Bessie, turning to Miss Abbot.

"But it was always in her," was the reply. "I've told Missis often my opinion about the child, and Missis agreed with me. She's an underhand little thing: I never saw a girl of her age with so much slyness."

Bessie answered not; but before long, addressing me, she said — "You ought to be aware, Miss, that you are under obligations to Mrs. Reed: she keeps you: if she were to turn you off, you would have to go to the poorhouse."

I had nothing to say to these words: they were not new to me: my very first recollections of existence included hints of the same kind. This pointed reminder of my dependence had become a vague sing-song in my ear: very painful and crushing, but only half intelligible.

Miss Abbot joined in: "And you ought not to think yourself on an equality with the Misses Reed and Master Reed, because Missis kindly allows you to be brought up with them. They will have a great deal of money, and you will have none: it is your place to be humble, and to try to make yourself agreeable to them."

"What we tell you is for your good," added Bessie, in no harsh voice, "you should try to be useful and pleasant, then, perhaps, you would have a home here; but if you become passionate and rude, Missis will send you away, I am sure."

"Besides," said Miss Abbot, "God will punish her: He might strike her dead in the midst of her tantrums, and then where would she go? Come, Bessie, we will leave her: I wouldn't have her heart for anything. Say your prayers, Miss Eyre, when you are by yourself; for if you don't repent, something bad might be permitted to come down the chimney and fetch you away."

They went, shutting the door, and locking it behind them.

An adapted extract from _Jane Eyre_ by Charlotte Brontë.

Consider

How do you think Jane will behave towards the maids, her cousin and Mrs Reed after this event? Why do you think that?

Year 6 Targeted Reading

Jane Eyre — Question Set 1

1 What has Jane Eyre done that is so shocking?

2B

....

2 Use the text to decide whether these statements are true or false.

2B

	True	False
There are two women holding Jane down.	☐	☐
Jane is tied down by garters.	☐	☐
This is the first time Jane has been told that she could get sent to the poorhouse.	☐	☐
Jane is advised to pray to God.	☐	☐

3 Draw lines to match the word taken from the text (left) with its correct definition (right).

2A

thrust	show regret
bonds	acting in a dishonest way
subsiding	becoming less intense
underhand	something used to tie things together
repent	pushed suddenly

Try replacing the word in the text with each of the definitions.

© *Not to be photocopied*

4 Read the text carefully to explain the different meanings of *Missis* and *Misses*.

2A

Missis	....
Misses	....

Scan the text for these words to help you find which part to read.

5 Using your own words, summarise what Bessie and Miss Abbot say to Jane from the paragraph beginning *Bessie answered not* to the end of the extract.

2C

....

....

....

....

....

6 Bessie and Miss Abbot warn Jane that she might be sent away.
Give two further consequences of her behaviour that they warn her about.

2B

1. ....

....

2. ....

....

Jane Eyre — Question Set 2

1 **Why do you think Jane is described as a *mad cat*?**

2G

✎

....

....

> You really need to picture the scene to answer this question.

2 **Find and copy the phrase in the extract that shows how quickly Jane wants to get away from the maids.**

2G

✎

....

3 **a)** **Who do you think is more sympathetic to Jane?**

2D

Tick one box

Bessie ☐

Miss Abbot ☐

They are equally sympathetic/
unsympathetic to Jane. ☐

b) **Use evidence from the text to justify your answer.**

2H

✎

....

....

....

....

4 Number the characters below in order of importance according to Miss Abbot and Bessie. Number them from 1 (most important) to 4 (least important).

2D

Mrs Reed ☐

Jane Eyre ☐

Master Reed ☐

Miss Abbot ☐

Consider the response when Jane asks if she is a servant.

5 Why do you think Miss Abbot and Bessie lock the door behind them at the end of the extract? Give two reasons.

2D

1. ....

....

2. ....

....

Look at what Miss Abbot says just before they lock Jane in.

Challenge

That Jane Eyre is clearly a nasty character. I bet she'll come to no good!

To what extent do you agree with this? Justify your answer using evidence from the text.

....

....

....

....

2E

Amazing Women

A biography tells you the story of somebody's life, usually a famous or important person. In the following extract from the book *Amazing Women*, written in 2018, Lucy Beevor presents an account of the life of Serena Williams, a professional tennis player.

Serena Williams was just a toddler when she first picked up a tennis racquet. Since then her career has been truly mind-boggling. Not only does she hold the record for the most Grand Slam singles titles of any modern player — male or female — but she has the most major titles in singles, doubles and mixed doubles combined among active players. She has been ranked World No. 1 for six years and counting, has four Olympic gold medals and has been described as 'the greatest player... that ever lived'.

Serena and her older sister, Venus, both showed a talent for tennis from an early age. Recognizing that the sisters had something special, their father Richard moved the family to Florida, USA, where the girls attended the Rick Macci Tennis Academy. Serena quickly made her mark on the junior tour, winning 46 of her 49 games and ranking No. 1 in the Florida under-10s. Tennis was becoming her life, but school was taking a back seat. Richard decided to pull the girls out of the academy to focus on schoolwork and began coaching them at home. This still involved gruelling two-hour daily training sessions to prepare the sisters for the professional stage.

In 1995, Serena entered her first professional tournament. She lost that match but two years later she started beating Top 10 players. In 1998, at the Australian Open, the Williams sisters met each other on the court for the first time in a Grand Slam tournament. Venus won that match but the loss made Serena even more determined to succeed. Just a year later, she won her first Grand Slam title at the US Open, kicking off a run of astonishing victories.

Serena transformed the women's game. Her sheer strength, power and attacking style allowed her to quickly overpower her opponents. Serena's forehand and double-backhand strokes are the most powerful in the women's game, while her blistering serve is the best of any female player in history. At the 2012 Wimbledon Championships, she hit a women's record of 102 aces, more than any male player hit during the tournament!

While Serena dominates on court, she is also one of the highest-paid female athletes off court. In 2016, she earned almost $30 million through endorsements, sponsorship and prize money.

But it hasn't all been easy. Not only has Serena faced injury and burnout but she has also dealt with surprising defeats. She credited her religious faith for reviving her inner champion and in 2017 she won her most historic game yet: she beat her sister in the final at the Australian Open to win her 23rd Grand Slam tournament while eight weeks pregnant! The victory saw her surpass Steffi Graf's previous record, sealing Serena's fate as one of sport's greatest-ever champions.

An extract from *Amazing Women* by Lucy Beevor.

Consider

**What are the differences between a biography and an autobiography?
If Serena Williams had written about herself how
do you think the extract would have been different?**

Amazing Women — Question Set 1

1 List three of Serena's achievements which have contributed towards her being described as *the greatest player... that ever lived.*

2D

1. ....

2. ....

3. ....

2 Complete the chart below to show the year or the event which happened.

2B

Date	Event
....	Serena entered her first professional tournament.
1998	....
....	She hit a women's record of 102 aces.
2016	....
2017	....

> Scan the text for words given in the table (e.g. years) to find the additional information you need.

3 Who won when Serena and her sister Venus played each other for the first time in a Grand Slam?

2B

....

2A

4 Match the words from the text (on the left) with a suitable synonym on the right.

mind-boggling	fierce
gruelling	exceed
blistering	breathtaking
dominates	demanding
surpass	controls

Remember to replace the word in the text with the given synonyms to see which sounds right.

Dictionary

2B

5 Serena and Venus's father, Richard, was concerned that their school work was suffering. What did he do about it?

....

....

2C

6 Read these statements carefully and decide if they are true or false. Tick your answers.

	True	False
Serena has had to work hard to be successful.	☐	☐
None of Serena's accomplishments have been better than any male tennis player's.	☐	☐
Both Serena's father and sister have motivated her at times.	☐	☐
Serena was successful at tennis even as a child.	☐	☐

To identify a statement as true, you will need to find evidence in the text to prove it.

Amazing Women — Question Set 2

1 Why do you think the author chose to use the words *Serena Williams was <u>just</u> a toddler* when she first picked up a tennis racquet?

2G

....

....

2 Re-read the two paragraphs starting from *Serena transformed the women's game*. Tick the statements below to show whether they are true or false.

2B

	True	False
Serena's forehand is more powerful than any other female player's.	☐	☐
In 2016, Serena earned almost $30m in prize money alone.	☐	☐
In 2012, Serena broke the men's and women's all-time records for the number of aces served.	☐	☐

3 What was the difference between Serena's experience at the Australian Open in 1998 and 2017?

2H

....

....

> When you're asked to <u>compare</u> two things, you have to mention them <u>both</u> in the answer.

4 Find and copy two phrases from the text which show that Serena's later career hasn't always seen her at the 'top of her game' (winning everything)?

2D

1. ....

2. ....

> The question says 'later career', so it's reasonable to search through the <u>second half</u> of the text for your answers to this one.

5 Serena Williams is known to have said she wants her daughter *to understand what it really means to be strong.* What do you think she means by this?

2D

....

....

....

....

....

....

> Do you think she means 'strong' physically, or do you think she means something else?

Challenge

Give three reasons why Serena Williams is a good choice to include in a book called 'Amazing Women'. Use evidence from the text to support your argument.

Reason	Evidence
1.	....
2.	....
3.	....

2D

Year 6 Targeted Reading

Answers

Text 1 — Autobiography

Pages 6 and 7: Working in the Warehouse — Question Set 1

1. first person

2. It was where jars of shoe polish (blacking) were made.

3. You should have given the stages the following numbers:
   Cover the pots with a piece of blue paper. — 2
   Tie the papers round with string. — 3
   Paste a printed label onto each pot. — 5
   Cover the pots with oil-paper. — 1
   Clip the paper close and neat all round. — 4

4. You should have matched these words to their definitions:
   abutting — next to
   wainscoted — panelled in wood
   apothecary — person who prepares drugs/medicines
   liberty — freedom
   scantiness — shortage

5. Any three of the following phrases:
   tumble-down old house, overrun with rats, rotten floors and staircases, old grey rats swarming, dirt and decay of the place

6. Answers could include reference to:
   • using money to pay for meals
   • working all day with others
   • being a shabby child
   • struggling to make money last
   • trying to save a certain amount of money per day
   • roaming the streets under-nourished/hungry
   • being thankful to God for not becoming a robber

Pages 8 and 9: Working in the Warehouse — Question Set 2

1. Any one of the following phrases:
   'as if I were there again'
   'I took the liberty of using his name, long afterwards, in Oliver Twist.'

2. There were only a few rats that lived in the warehouse. — false
   Before applying labels, Charles Dickens had to cover a large number of pots with paper first. — true
   Charles Dickens tried to ration out his wages. — true
   Charles Dickens became a robber. — false

3. Examples:
   Bob Fagin made an impression on Dickens.
   Dickens must have found his experiences at the blacking warehouse hard to forget.
   Fagin is an unusual name.

4. You should have ticked: It describes how he felt about working at the warehouse.

5. a) He really didn't like it OR It made him miserable OR He thought it was awful

b) Any three of the following phrases:
   the secret agony of my soul, being utterly neglected and hopeless, shame I felt in my position, of the misery it was to my young heart

Challenge
   Example:
   Why the bird is wrong: Charles Dickens found working in the warehouse shameful not fun and he wasn't even paid enough money to eat well even though he worked long hours.
   Evidence: 'the shame I felt in my position', 'the misery it was to my young heart', 'insufficiently and unsatisfactorily fed', 'I worked, from morning to night'

Text 2 — Persuasive Text

Pages 12 and 13: Waste Warriors — Question Set 1

1. It was a versatile material that never decomposed or decayed.

2. You should have matched these pairs:
   The Plastisphere is the name given to the miles and miles of plastic, and the creatures that live on it, which appear like floating — islands.
   Eating plastic can poison, injure and kill both sea and land — creatures.
   The Waste Warriors movement aims to encourage children to join their — mission.
   This text encourages you to use less single-use plastic, like water bottles, utensils and disposable — containers.
   A link to their website is provided so that children can register their — interest.

3. Any two of the following words: damage, death, littered, blight, danger

4. You should have ticked: what can be done to help save the Earth from further damage

5. Any three of the following: reduce how much single-use plastic they use, encourage friends and family to do the same, join Waste Warriors, register their interest online

6. Approximately 8 million pieces of plastic waste are floating around our oceans. — Fact
   The author believes that plastic waste has caused a massive blight on our surroundings. — Fact
   Everyone should do something to help fight against the damage caused by plastic. — Opinion
   Floating islands of plastic waste and the creatures that live on them are called the Plastisphere. — Fact

Pages 14 and 15: Waste Warriors — Question Set 2

1. Example:
   to get the reader thinking (about their own feelings about waste and the environment) OR to involve the reader

2. Example:

Author's feelings:	Evidence from the text:
1. worry	'causing untold damage and death'
2. anger	'engulf our amazing oceans'

Answers

3. 'our amazing oceans', 'beautiful countryside'

4. They want to draw your attention to the picture.
   OR It heightens the impact, and makes you think how bad it could be.

5. You should have ticked: All of the words show how bad the problem is.

Challenge
Example.

What I think:	I think the octopus is wrong.
Why I think it:	The text tells children what they can do and what is suggested isn't dangerous.
Evidence from text:	'reduce the amount of single-use plastic you use' 'encourage your friends and family to do the same' Repetition of 'you can'

Text 3 — Classic Fiction

Pages 18 and 19: Kidnapped — Question Set 1

1. To fetch a chest for his uncle.

2. 'blacker than ever', 'colour of the darkness', 'went black again', 'feel along the wall'

3. There was no sound of wind or thunder before it happened.

4. You should have matched these pairs:
   lowermost — bottom
   aloft — skyward
   minding — recalling
   breaches — openings
   confounded — perplexed

5. a) You should have ticked: personification

   b) Examples:
   I think it means he was so frightened that he couldn't speak. OR I think it means that it felt like he was being 'gripped at his throat' because of his fear.

6. Example:

How David felt:	He dislikes them and doesn't like the sound they make.
How I know:	He calls them 'foul beasts' and says his ears are 'troubled' by the sound of them.

Pages 20 and 21: Kidnapped — Question Set 2

1. lightning

2. You should have circled: threatened

3. Example:
   It's like the wind has blown courage into him but also anger because his uncle has sent him there. A gust suggests it's a sudden feeling that has come upon him.

4. You should have ticked:
   dazed, afraid, angry, distracted

5. a) You should have circled: No

   b) Your answer may refer to:
   the danger David is in:
   • Going out into the dark with no light
   • Going up steps that are in the open air
   • Being bombarded by bats
   the end of the text:
   • The openness at the top of the tower
   • No sign of a chest
   David's own feelings:
   • 'certainly to run great risks'
   • 'perhaps to die'

Challenge
Answers should be based on what has happened so far in this extract. Examples:
Agree — He is determined to complete the job, as he says he has an 'angry courage', and says 'I swore I would settle that "perhaps"'.
Disagree — He is 'angry' with his uncle for putting his life at risk, so may not want to help him by bringing down the chest.
Disagree — It will be too dangerous to carry a chest down quickly as the steps are 'steep and narrow'.

Text 4 — Quest Story

Pages 24 and 25: The Story of the Amulet — Question Set 1

1. a charm

2. The light came after the voice. — false
   At first the light was lovely and large. — false
   The children were surprised how dark it was. — true
   The light came from many glow-worms. — false

3. 'nightingales', 'the sea', 'the fiddle', 'the voice of your mother when you have been a long time away'

4. You should have ticked: illumination

5. Example:
   Because the voice tells them that it has been smashed up into tiny pieces which are scattered all over the land.

6. You should have given the events the following numbers:
   Cyril is confused. — 5
   The children are in darkness. — 1
   Cyril and Robert react to the voice's explanation of what happened to the Amulet. — 4
   The light grows stronger. — 2
   The voice begins to speak more loudly. — 3

Pages 26 and 27: The Story of the Amulet — Question Set 2

1. a) 'dark', 'darker', 'darkest'

   b) Example:
   Using the word 'dark' repeatedly emphasises how dark it really is. 'Darkest' makes it seem like it's pitch black.

2. The light is compared to glow-worms.

Answers

3. Examples:
   Effect: It made them think of nice things.
   Evidence: 'It was like nightingales, and the sea, and the fiddle, and the voice of your mother...'
   OR Effect: They were overcome with happiness.
   Evidence: It made them want to 'cry with pleasure'.
   OR Effect: They were hypnotised.
   Evidence: 'No one cared to speak', and they looked 'at the green radiance'.

4. You should have ticked: A place which is sacred or holy.

5. Your answer may mention:
   • the beautiful light (how it makes you feel/its colour etc.)
   • the hypnotic voice (unknown but understood language/beautiful sound)
   • made of two parts joined by a pin
   • held in a shrine

Challenge
   Example:
   There is no way the children will be able to collect all the dust as it is scattered over many lands and sunk into many seas. The voice is suggesting that the only way they'll find it is by going back to a time when it was perfect and whole: 'You must seek it where it still is, perfect as ever...In the Past you may find it'.

Text 5 — Non-Chronological Report

Pages 30 and 31: Air Raids — Question Set 1

1. The table should be filled in like this:

Britain	Germany
United States	Japan OR Germany
Japan	Australia
Germany	Britain

2. The bombers from Japan and Germany could not fly that far.

3. You should have matched these pairs:
   Londoners — slept in the underground tube stations of the city.
   German children — were held at shoulder height in the shelters.
   The German Luftwaffe — began bombing London in September 1940.
   British children — continued to go to school during the day.
   German people — were crowded and uncomfortable in the U-Bahn stations.

4. German children found the war much harder to deal with than British children. — Opinion
   Some people chose to stay in their homes during air raids. — Fact
   It was really unfair that some people had to sleep in caves when others got to sleep in air raid shelters. — Opinion
   More Japanese people were killed than British people. — Fact
   America was the luckiest country during World War II. — Opinion

5. extensively — heavily
   widespread — mass
   packed — crammed, crowded
   peak — climax

6. The two cities were completely destroyed by the atomic bombs.

Pages 32 and 33: Air Raids — Question Set 2

1. Examples:
   'There were fears that...' — It shows how bombing raids affected people's everyday lives.
   'German children experienced...' — It tells us how uncomfortable and dangerous the air raids were for German children.

2. Examples:
   Different Types of Air Raid Shelters
   OR Air Raid Shelters used in World War II

3. Any two of the following:
   'mass air attacks destroyed cities', 'Japan suffered heavy bombing', 'experienced the terrors of air raids', 'damage thousands of houses and many schools', 'kill at least 30,000 people', 'wipe out the Japanese cities'

4. Your answer should refer to people interested in World War II or air raids. You should also mention what life was like for children during the war/in the past, as much of the text focuses on children, and the report is taken from a book called 'Children in Wartime'.

5. Your answer may refer to some or all of the following:
   • They were 'almost constantly' bombed in 1944-1945.
   • Sometimes the air was so bad in the shelter, people had to leave even when bombs were falling.
   • Allied air forces (countries working together) began 'round-the-clock bombing of Germany'.
   • The Allies bombed the German city of Dresden.

Challenge
   Your answer may agree, disagree or have elements of both.
   Reasons for agreeing:
   • At the start of the war it might have felt exciting and like an adventure.
   • When inside the shelter there might have been other children to play with which would be fun.
   Reasons for disagreeing:
   • The German children often had to be held up high in the shelters because there was such a lack of oxygen.
   • It would have been really frightening for children, not knowing if their house or school would survive the bombing.
   • The shelters were sometimes very cramped so there wouldn't have been anywhere to play and children wouldn't have their toys or friends with them.

Answers

Text 6 — Flashback Story

Pages 36 and 37: The Girl of Ink & Stars — Question Set 1

1. You should have matched these pairs:
   The Governor's house — Between the sea and the forest
   The school — Between the Governor's house and the village
   The orchard — Further away from the beach than the Governor's house
   The beaches covered by the tide — To the west
   The clay mines — Above the beaches

2. Isabella now goes to the same school as Lupe.

3. You should have ticked: squinted

4. You should have put these events in the following order:
   Isabella remembers being at the clay mines. — 4
   Isabella laughs so hard it hurts. — 1
   Isabella's Ma dies. — 2
   Gabo dies. — 3

5. simile: 'like a mountain'
   personification: 'crouched'

6. Your answer should mention at least three of the following:
   • Being with her Ma and Gabo at the mines
   • Having fun
   • Learning to tie themselves to the dragon tree
   • Being lowered into the gorge
   • Gabo being scared
   • Gabo falling
   • Laughing
   • The ache in her belly
   • Ma dying
   • Gabo dying

Pages 38 and 39: The Girl of Ink & Stars — Question Set 2

1. The Governor is rich. — true
   Lupe is popular at school. — false
   Isabella feels sorry for Lupe. — true
   Isabella wants to swim in the sea. — true
   Ma and Gabo die of different diseases. — false

2. It shows how small they look because they are so far away.

3. a) Because they blame her for not being able to paint the walls rainbow coloured in the new school.

   b) Example:
   Lupe thinks her Dad does things to make the family appear better than everyone else 'To uphold the family honour'. She doesn't say this like she is proud of it because she puts on a posh voice so it's like she disagrees with it. She also speaks with a 'sad smile' when she tries to explain that it has not been done for her so maybe she'd like her Dad to love her more.

4. 'My toes itched', 'it was not the same as trying it for myself'

5. Example:
   The first quote is literal — referring to Ma bringing Gabo up from the dark of the gorge. The second quote is metaphorical/figurative/not literal — referring to the darkness Isabella felt when Ma died and no one could help her.

Challenge
   Your answer should say whether you agree or disagree with the jellyfish.
   Your answer may refer to the way Isabella describes different parts of the island — the size of the Governor's house, the colour of the sea and the forest, how the school has changed.
   Your answer should mention that Isabella tries not to look at the clay mines and explain this is because it is such a sad memory because both Ma and Gabo are now dead.

Text 7 — Explanation Text

Pages 42 and 43: Lasers — Question Set 1

1. It turns it into a straight, narrow beam of very bright light.

2. Concentrated and very powerful.
   It is of one colour only or invisible infra-red rays.

3. You should have matched these pairs:
   medium — substance
   orbiting — revolving around
   partially — not completely
   illuminates — lights up

4. Lasers are used by scientists to study the Earth. — true
   Lasers only have one important job to do. — false
   Lasers have only been discovered in the last 20 years. — false
   Laser light waves are different to ordinary light waves. — true

5. Examples:
   The subheadings help the reader know what they're going to read about in each section. OR They help to organise the writing into sections.

6. Any three of the following examples:
   • 'increasing our knowledge about our planet'
   • 'first used in surgery'
   • 'used to measure Earth's movements'
   • 'First transatlantic optical fibres send telephone messages'
   • 'Laser-guided missiles used by USA in Gulf War'
   • measuring the 'distance from the Moon to the Earth'
   • 'measure distances accurately'
   • 'make holograms and compact discs'
   • 'guide missiles'
   • 'detect earthquakes and volcanic eruptions'
   • 'plane powered by lasers'
   • 'laser headlights'

Answers

Pages 44 and 45: Lasers — Question Set 2

1. Even though it is three-dimensional, it is not solid so it is like a ghost. OR It is see-through or transparent like a ghost.
    You can't say 'it is like a ghost' on its own, as this is given in the text.

2. Example: When the films were made, laser weapons weren't available yet so they were considered futuristic.

3. are spread out so less powerful — ordinary light
    can be one colour only — laser light
    can travel far and stay concentrated — laser light
    reinforce each other — laser light
    do not all follow the same path — ordinary light

4. Any two of the following examples:
    • The numbers link the explanation of how holograms are made and viewed to the different stages shown in the diagrams/figures.
    • The letters A and B are used to label the two diagrams/figures about recording and viewing holograms.
    • The colour of the reference beam in Figure B is the same as the reference beam in Figure A.
    • The direction the light travels is described in the text, and shown by arrows in the diagram.
    • The diagrams/figures show the reader how holograms are created.

5. *Example answer:*
    The laser was first developed in 1960 and has since been put to a variety of uses, including surgery and weaponry. Tiny, high-powered microlasers were developed in 1998. More recently, lasers have been used to amplify sounds.

    Challenge
    Example:
    What I think: I don't agree.
    Why I think it: Because lasers do many more important jobs than just being used in weapons in films.
    Evidence from the text: The text says that lasers have been used to help scientists to find out more about our planet, the Moon, earthquakes and volcanic eruptions. They've even been used in surgery and to help guide missiles in war.

Text 8 — Classic Fiction

Pages 48 and 49: Jane Eyre — Question Set 1

1. She has struck/hit a young gentleman/her master/her cousin.

2. There are two women holding Jane down. — True
    Jane is tied down by garters. — False
    This is the first time Jane has been told that she could get sent to the poorhouse. — False
    Jane is advised to pray to God. — True

3. You should have matched these pairs:
    thrust — pushed suddenly
    bonds — something used to tie things together
    subsiding — becoming less intense
    underhand — acting in a dishonest way
    repent — show regret

4. Missis — Mrs Reed (Miss Abbot is her maid)
    Misses — Mrs Reed's daughters (the plural of Miss Reed)

5. Your answer should refer to at least two of the following:
    • Mrs Reed will send Jane to a poorhouse if she makes her angry.
    • Jane is not equal to Mrs Reed's children.
    • Jane will not have money.
    • Jane should behave well if she wishes to stay.
    • She should pray to God for forgiveness.

6. God will strike her dead
    something bad will take her away

Pages 50 and 51: Jane Eyre — Question Set 2

1. Your answer should refer to a particular aspect of a cat's behaviour. Examples:
    Jane might be using her nails to scratch them (like a cat uses its claws).
    She could be making screeching noises (like a cat fighting).

2. 'rise from it like a spring'

3. a) You may pick any answer for this question provided you can justify your choice in part b).
    b) Your answer should refer to both women to show a comparison.
    Examples:
    (*Bessie*) Bessie is more sympathetic to her because later in the text it says she spoke to her 'in no harsh voice' whereas Miss Abbot says cruel things about Jane being punished.
    (*Miss Abbot*) Miss Abbot is more sympathetic to her because it is Bessie that suggests she is tied down and Miss Abbot just does what she is told in removing the garter from her leg.
    (*Equal*) They are equally unsympathetic to her because they both show their horror at Jane having hit her cousin, and refer to her 'shocking conduct' and 'your wickedness'. They both force her onto the stool. They also both warn her that if she doesn't behave properly she'll be sent away.

4. You should have given these people the following numbers:
    Mrs Reed — 1
    Jane Eyre — 4
    Master Reed — 2
    Miss Abbot — 3

5. Any two of the following:
    so that Jane could not escape, to reflect on her actions, to say her prayers

    Challenge
    Example:
    I do not agree that she is a nasty character because her bad behaviour can be explained by the fact that she is poorly treated. For example, she is called 'less than a servant'. I also disagree that she will come to no good because she shows a lot of courage. For example, she copes with the maids' threats by turning them into a 'sing-song' in her ear.

Answers

Text 9 — Biography

Pages 54 and 55: Amazing Women — Question Set 1

1. You could have mentioned:
   • She has the most Grand Slam singles titles of any modern player.
   • She was ranked World No. 1 for six years.
   • She has four Olympic Gold medals.
   • She has the most major titles in combined types.
   • She hit a record number of aces at Wimbledon in 2012.

2. The table should be filled in like this:

Date	Event
1995	Serena entered her first professional tournament.
1998	**Venus and Serena met each other for the first time in a Grand Slam tournament.**
2012	She hit a women's record of 102 aces.
2016	**She earned almost $30 million.**
2017	**She beat her sister at the Australian Open (winning her 23rd Grand Slam tournament).**

3. Venus

4. You should have matched these pairs:
   mind-boggling — breathtaking
   gruelling — demanding
   blistering — fierce
   dominates — controls
   surpass — exceed

5. Example:
   He took them out of the tennis academy they were in to focus on school work and coached them at home.

6. Serena has had to work hard to be successful. — true
   None of Serena's accomplishments have been better than any male tennis player's. — false
   Both Serena's father and sister have motivated her at times. — true
   Serena was successful at tennis even as a child. — true

Pages 56 and 57: Amazing Women — Question Set 2

1. Example:
   The word 'just' emphasises how young she was when she started playing tennis.

2. Serena's forehand is more powerful than any other female player's. — true
   In 2016, Serena earned almost $30m in prize money alone. — false
   In 2012, Serena broke the men's and women's all-time records for the number of aces served. — false

3. In 1998, Serena lost to her sister, whereas in 2017 she beat her.

4. Your answer should mention two of the following phrases:
   • 'But it hasn't all been easy'
   • 'Not only has Serena faced injury and burnout'
   • 'she has also dealt with surprising defeats'

5. Your answers may refer to the following:
   • not just having strong arms / legs / serve
   • not just being able to hit the ball really hard
   • strength of mind
   • being able to keep going when things are tough
   • having a strong belief in yourself
   • being determined

Challenge
Examples:

Reason	Evidence
She is very determined.	She lost her first professional match, but went on to beat Top 10 players just two years later.
She has done a lot for women's tennis.	She has beaten men's records — she hit more aces in a tournament than any of the men.
She is one of the most successful sportspeople in the world.	She is 'one of sport's greatest-ever champions'.

Acknowledgements:

p.10-11: Waste Warriors by Maxine Petrie
p.16: Graphic © iStock.com/heather_mcgrath
p.28-29: Excerpted from the work entitled: Children During Wartime © 2005 by Capstone. All rights reserved.
p.28: Photo © Bettmann / Contributor / Bettmann / Getty Images
p.34-35: The Girl of Ink and Stars. Text © Kiran Millwood Hargrave 2016. Reproduced with permission of Chicken House Ltd. All rights reserved
p.40-41: Adapted extract from The Encyclopaedia of Science published by Aladdin Books.
p.52-53: Extract from AMAZING WOMEN by Lucy Beevor. Reproduced by permission of Stripes Publishing Limited. Text copyright © Lucy Beevor 2018.
     Illustrations copyright © Sarah Green 2018.

Pages 3 and 64 contain public sector information licensed under the Open Government Licence v3.0. http://www.nationalarchives.gov.uk/doc/open-government-licence/version/3/

Images & Clipart throughout the book from Corel ® and Clipart.com

National Curriculum Content Areas

Use the table below to record how pupils are doing in each of the National Curriculum Content Areas.

National Curriculum Content Areas

Text	Set	2a Word Meaning	2b Retrieval	2c Summarising	2d Inference	2e Prediction	2f Text Meaning	2g Language	2h Comparison
Text 1: Working in the Warehouse	Set 1	Q4	Q3 Q6		Q2		Q5b	Q5	
	Set 2		Q1 Q2 Q5		Q2 Q3 Q4 Q5a Ch		Q6	Q1	
Text 2: Waste Warriors	Set 1		Q1	Q4	Q3 Q5b Q6		Q1 Q5	Q2 Q3 Q4	Q4
	Set 2								
Text 3: Kidnapped	Set 1	Q4	Q1 Q2 Q3 Q5	Q6	Q1 Q5a Q5b		Q2	Q3 Q5a	Q3
	Set 2	Q4	Q1a Q2	Q2					
Text 4: The Story of the Amulet	Set 1	Q4	Q1 Q2 Q3	Q5	Q3			Q1b	
	Set 2	Q5							
Text 5: Air Raids	Set 1	Q5	Q1 Q2 Q3	Q1 Q2	Ch			Q3	Q5
	Set 2		Q1 Q2 Q6	Ch				Q6	
Text 6: The Girl of Ink & Stars	Set 1	Q3	Q1 Q2	Q4	Q1 Q3b Ch	Ch	Q4	Q6	Q3b
	Set 2	Q3	Q3a						
Text 7: Lasers	Set 1	Q3	Q1 Q2	Q4	Q2		Q4 Q5	Q5	Q3
	Set 2								
Text 8: Jane Eyre	Set 1	Q3 Q4	Q1 Q2 Q6	Q5 Ch	Q3a Q4 Q5	Ch	Q4 Q5	Q1 Q2	Q3
	Set 2	Q3	Q2 Q3 Q5						
Text 9: Amazing Women	Set 1	Q4	Q2	Q6	Q4 Q5 Ch			Q1	Q3
	Set 2								
Total									